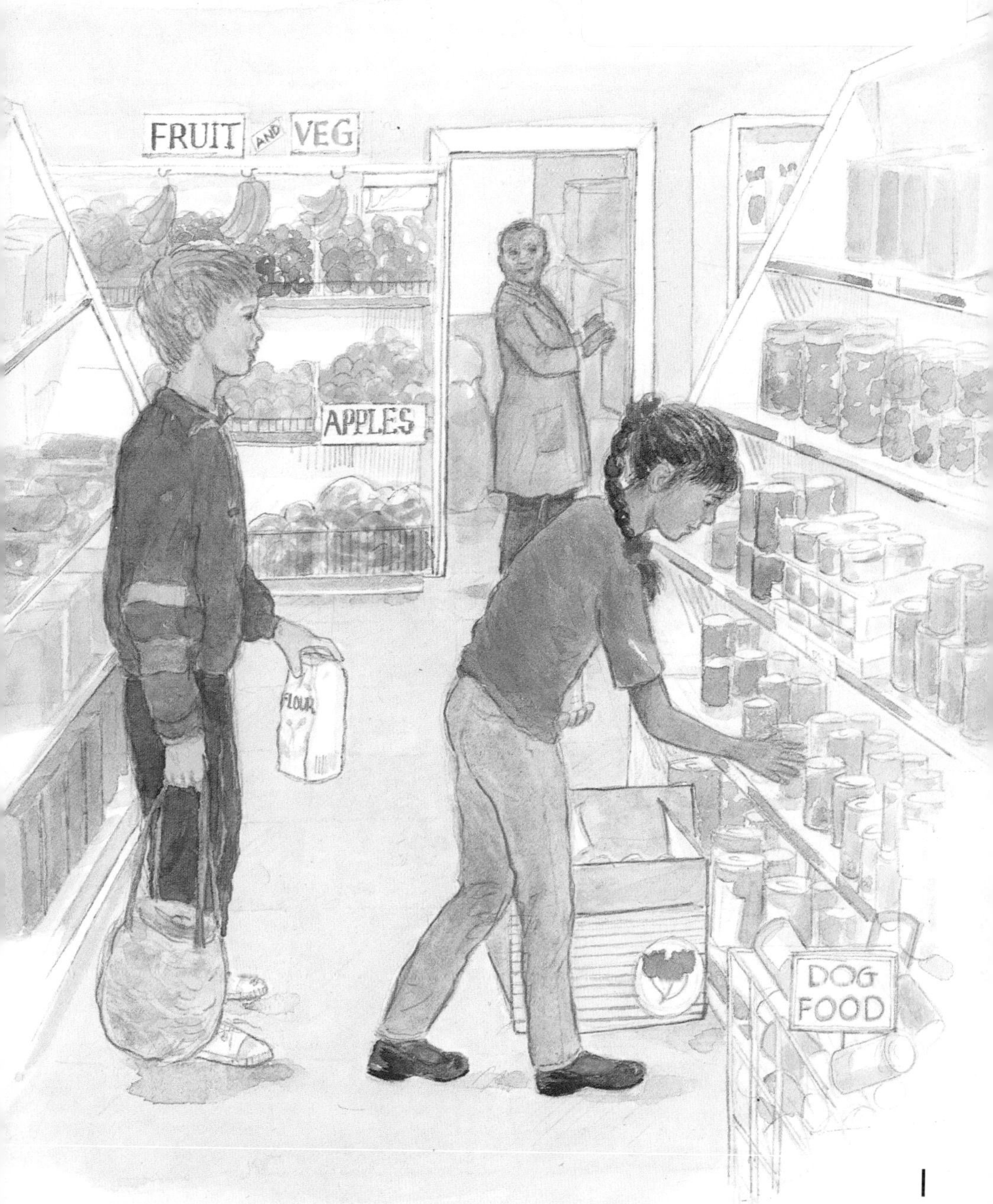
FRUIT AND VEG
APPLES
FLOUR
DOG FOOD

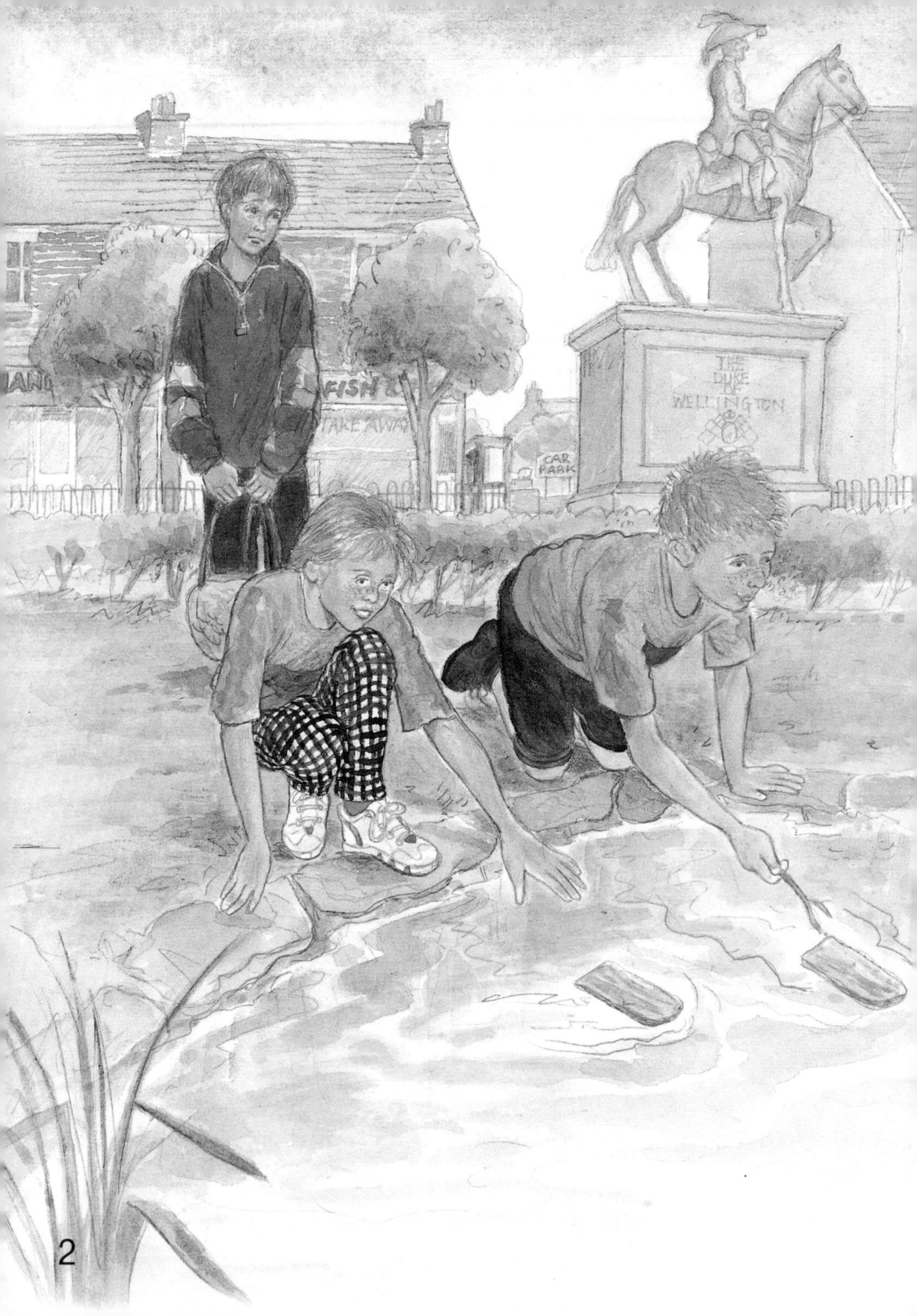

FISH
TAKE AWAY
CAR PARK
THE DUKE OF WELLINGTON

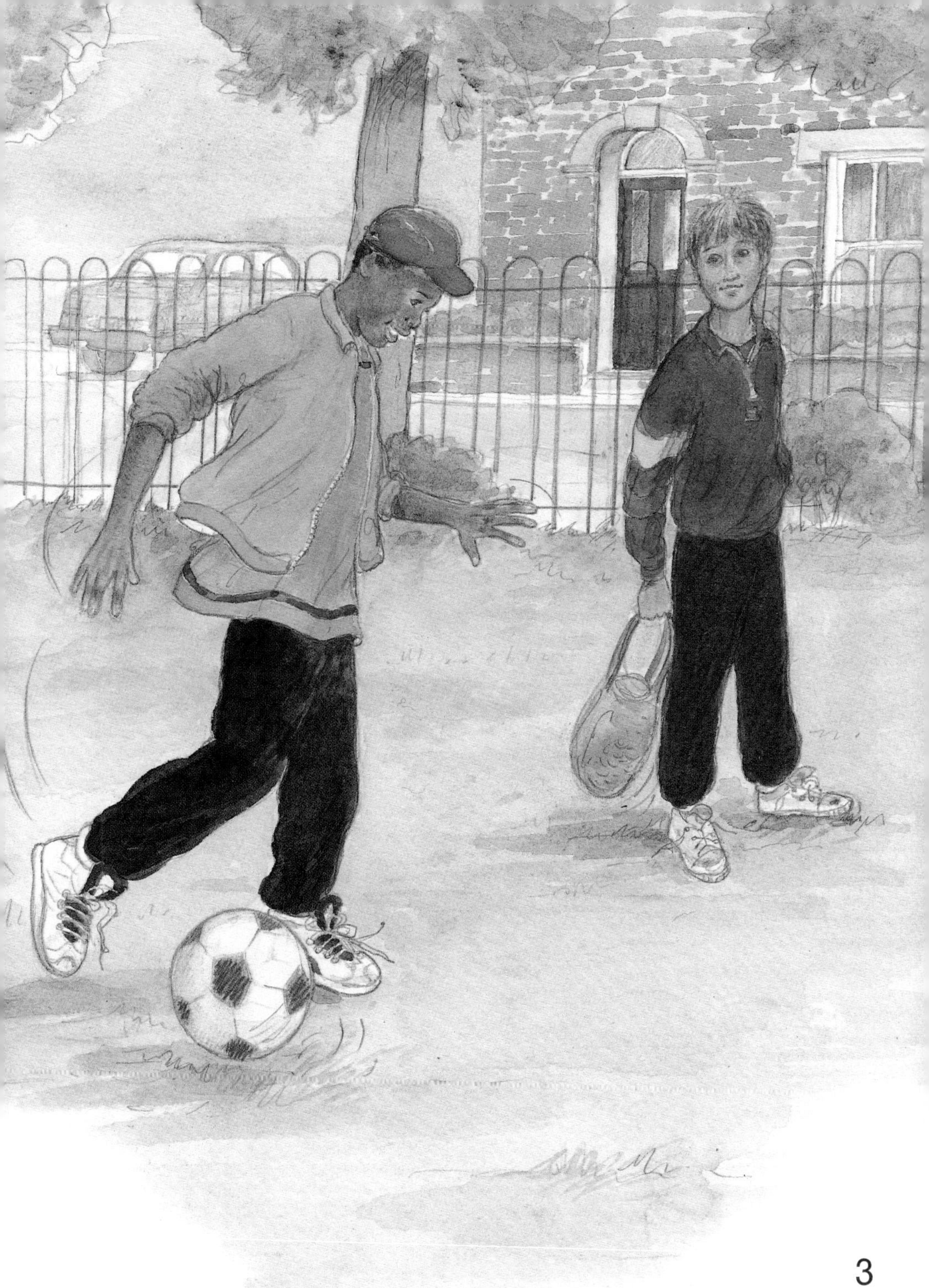

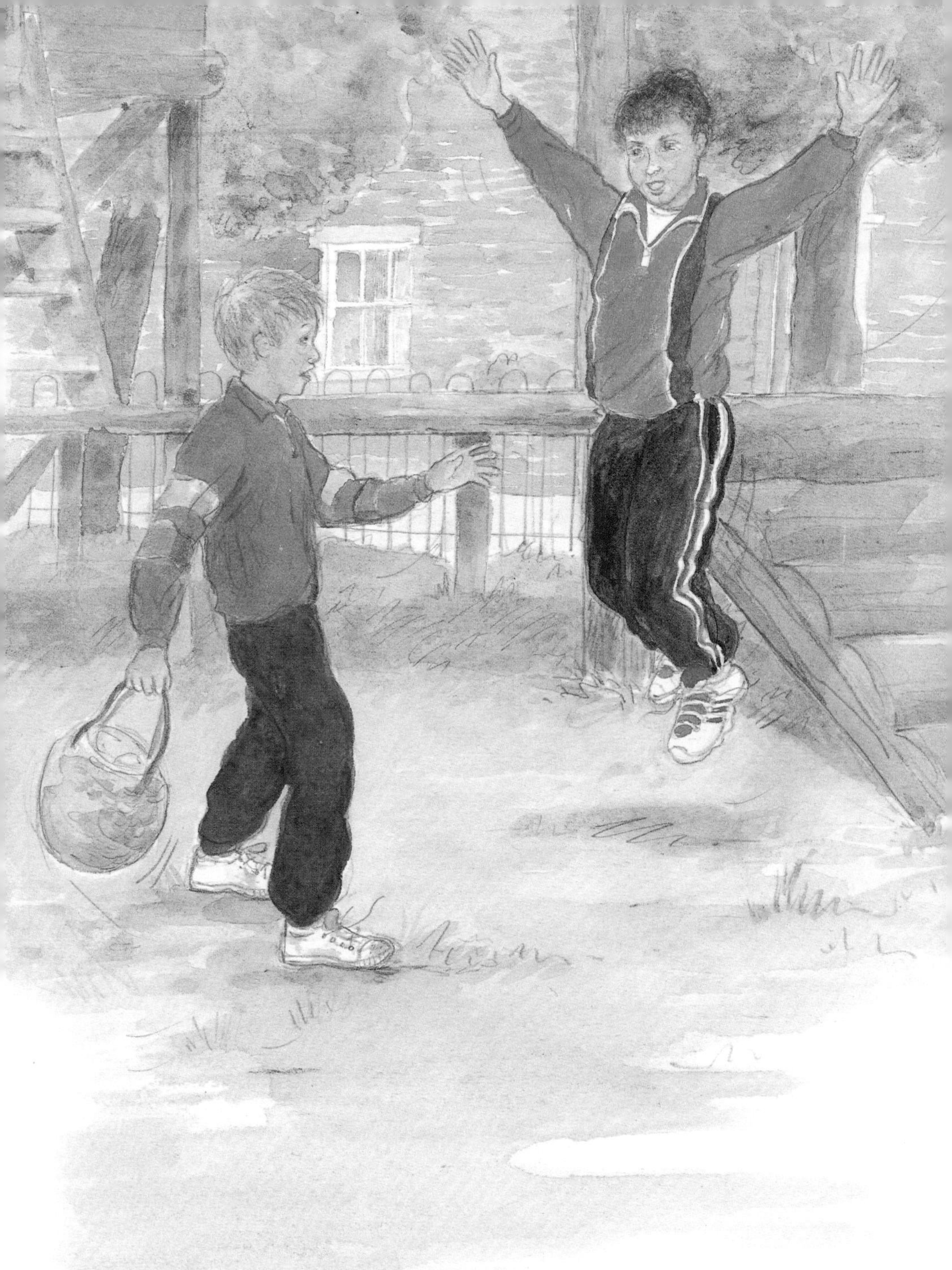

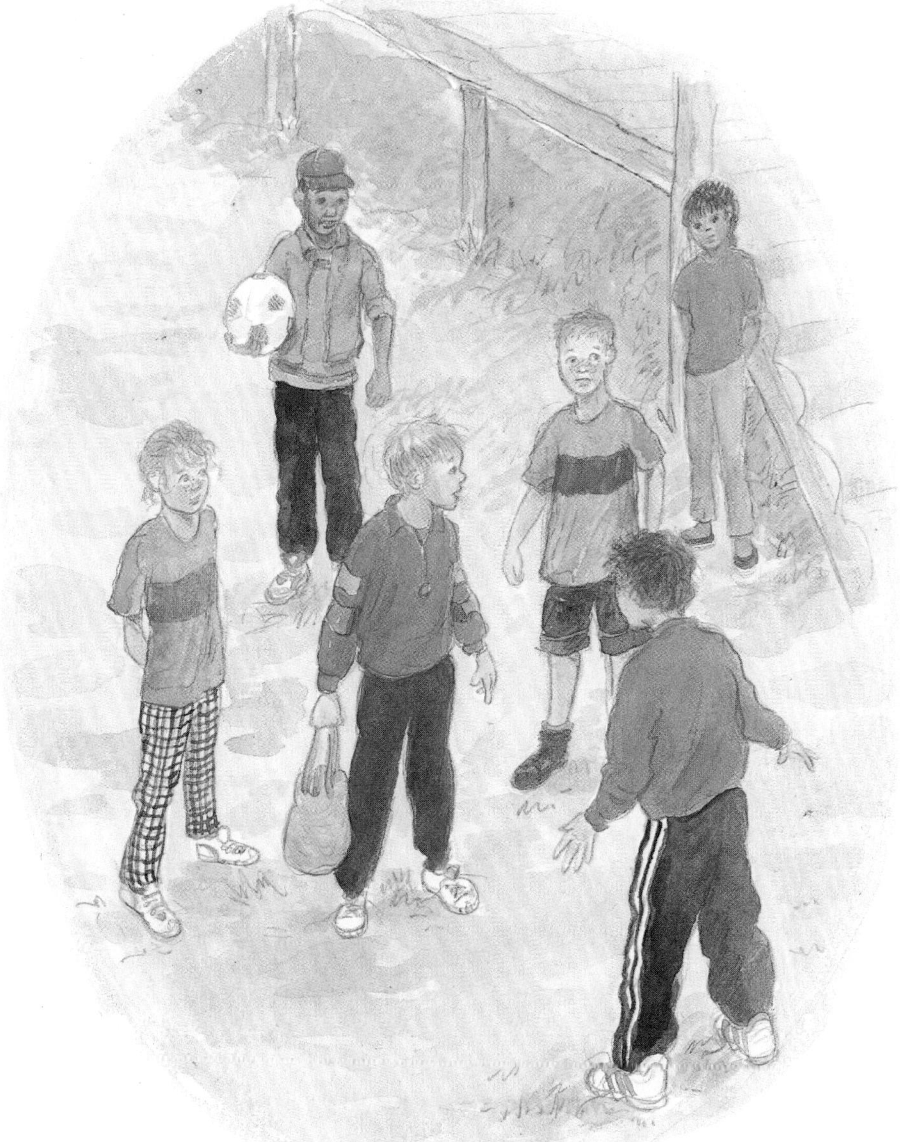

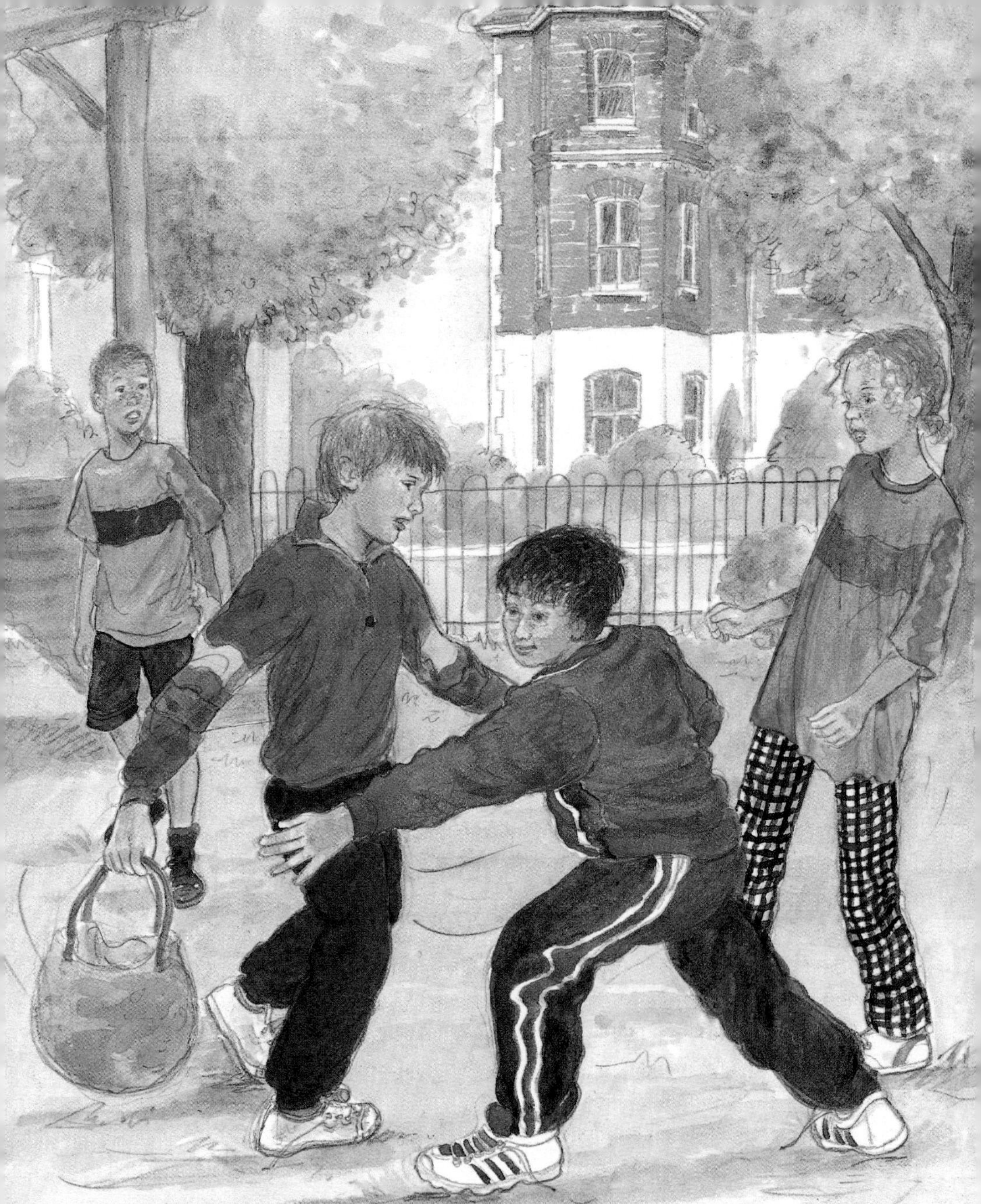

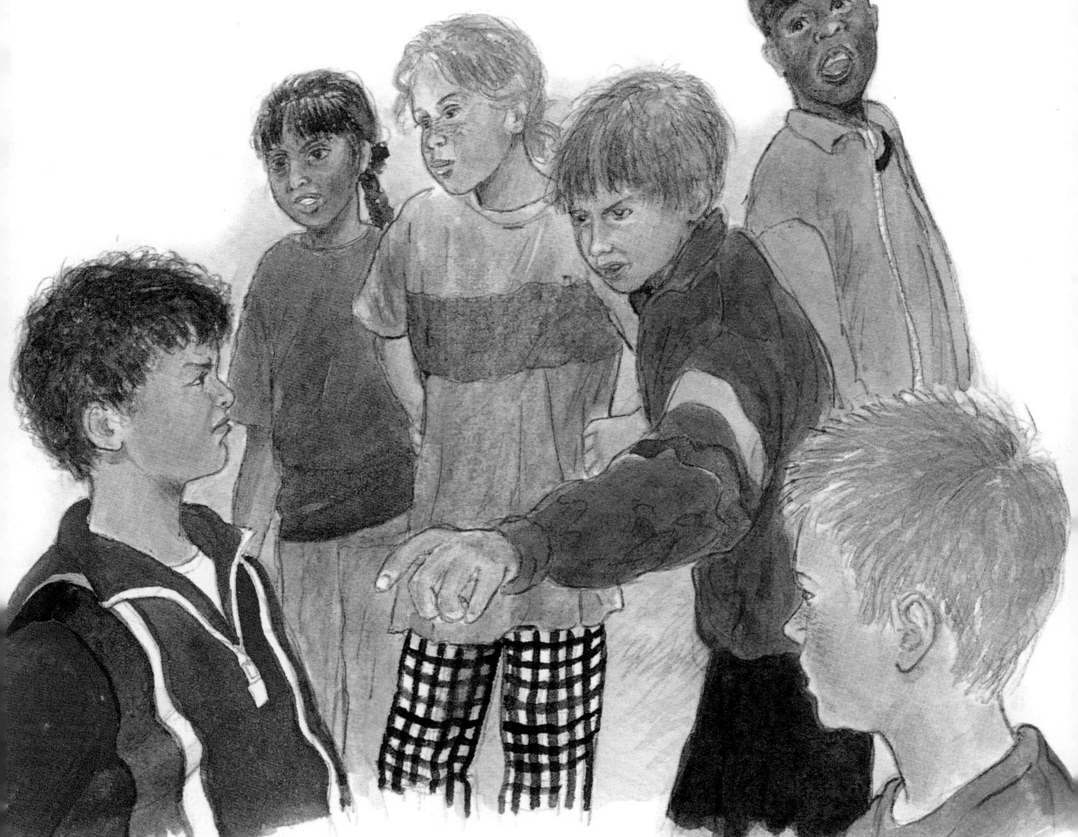

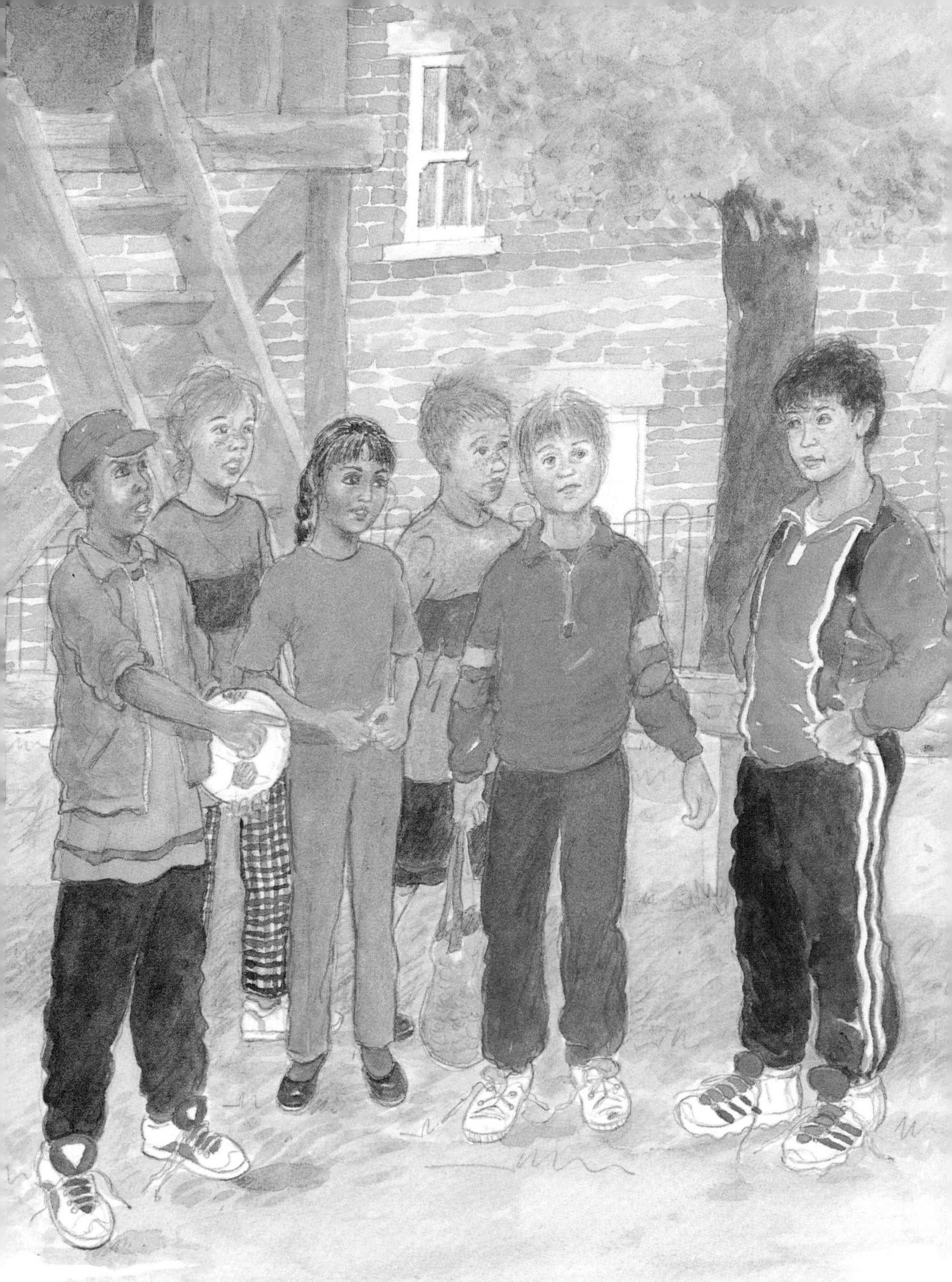

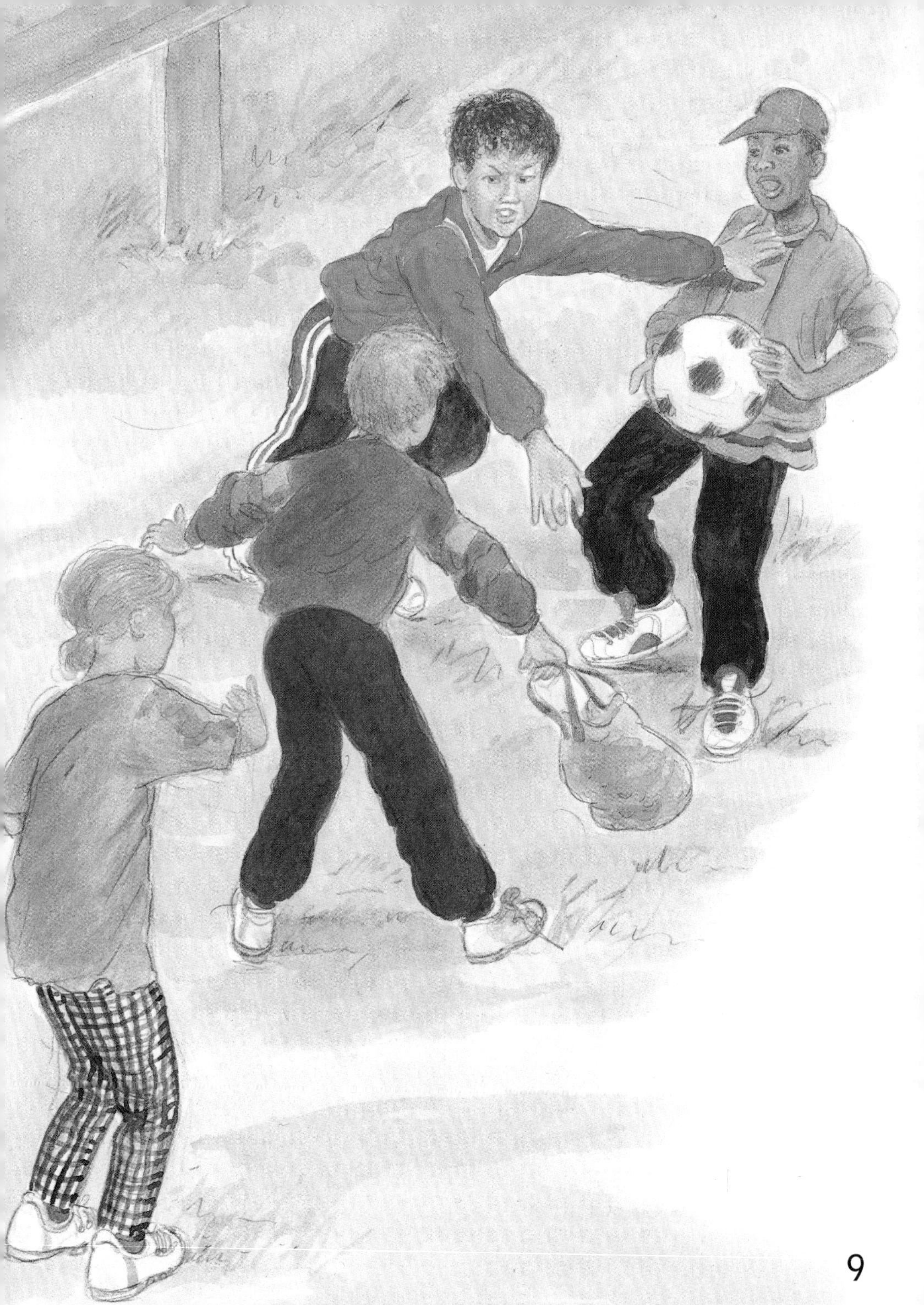

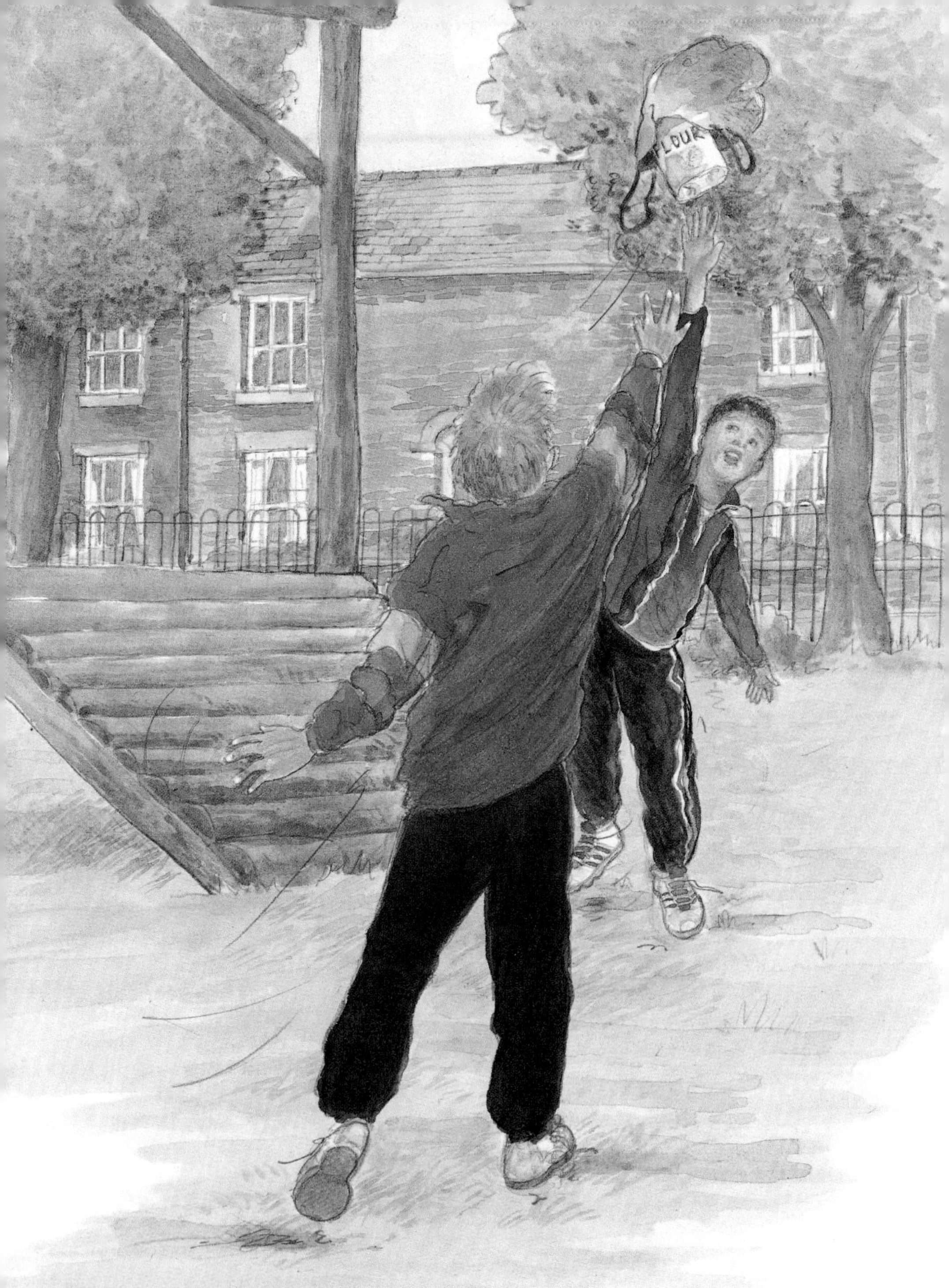
FLOUR

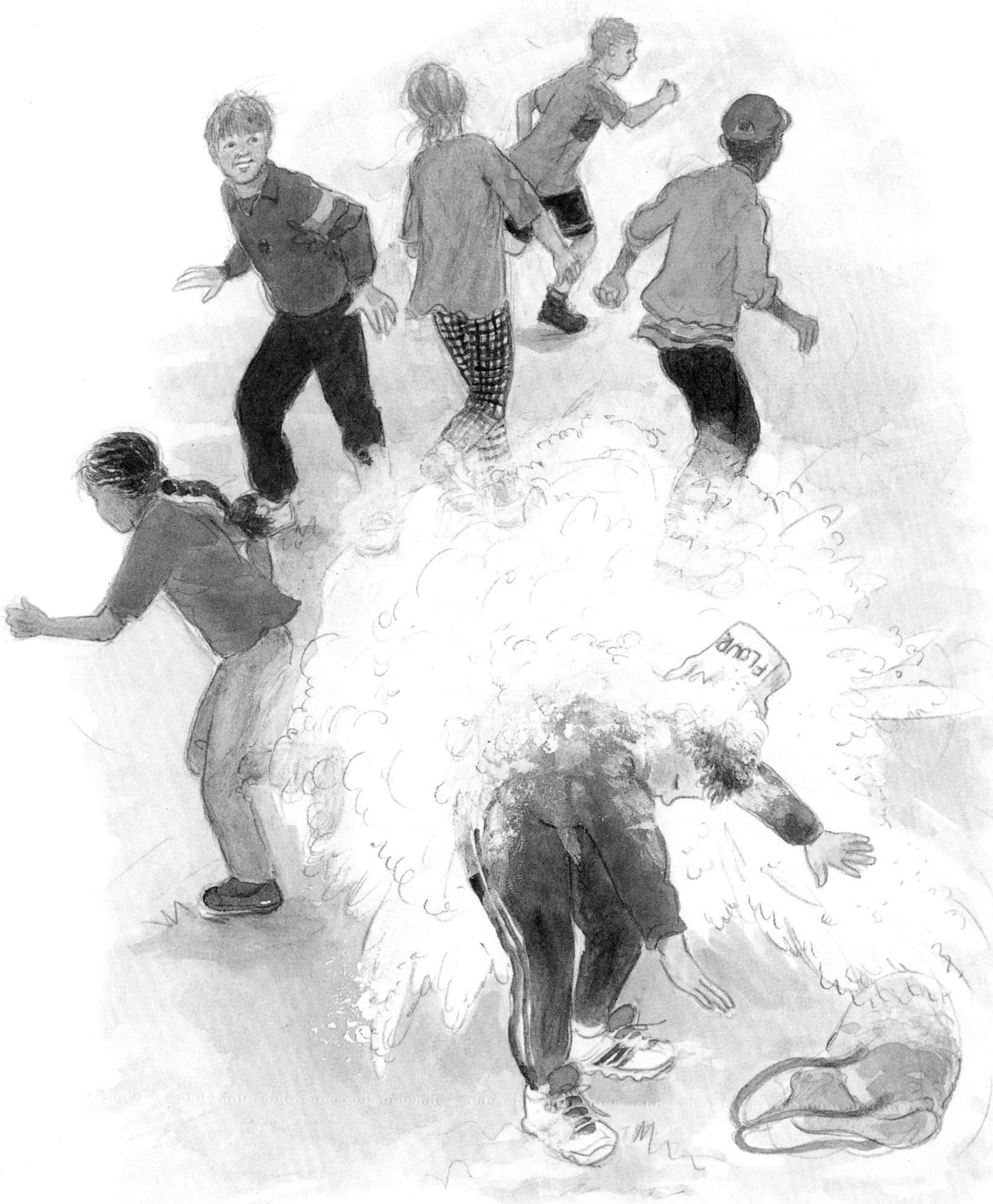
FLOUR

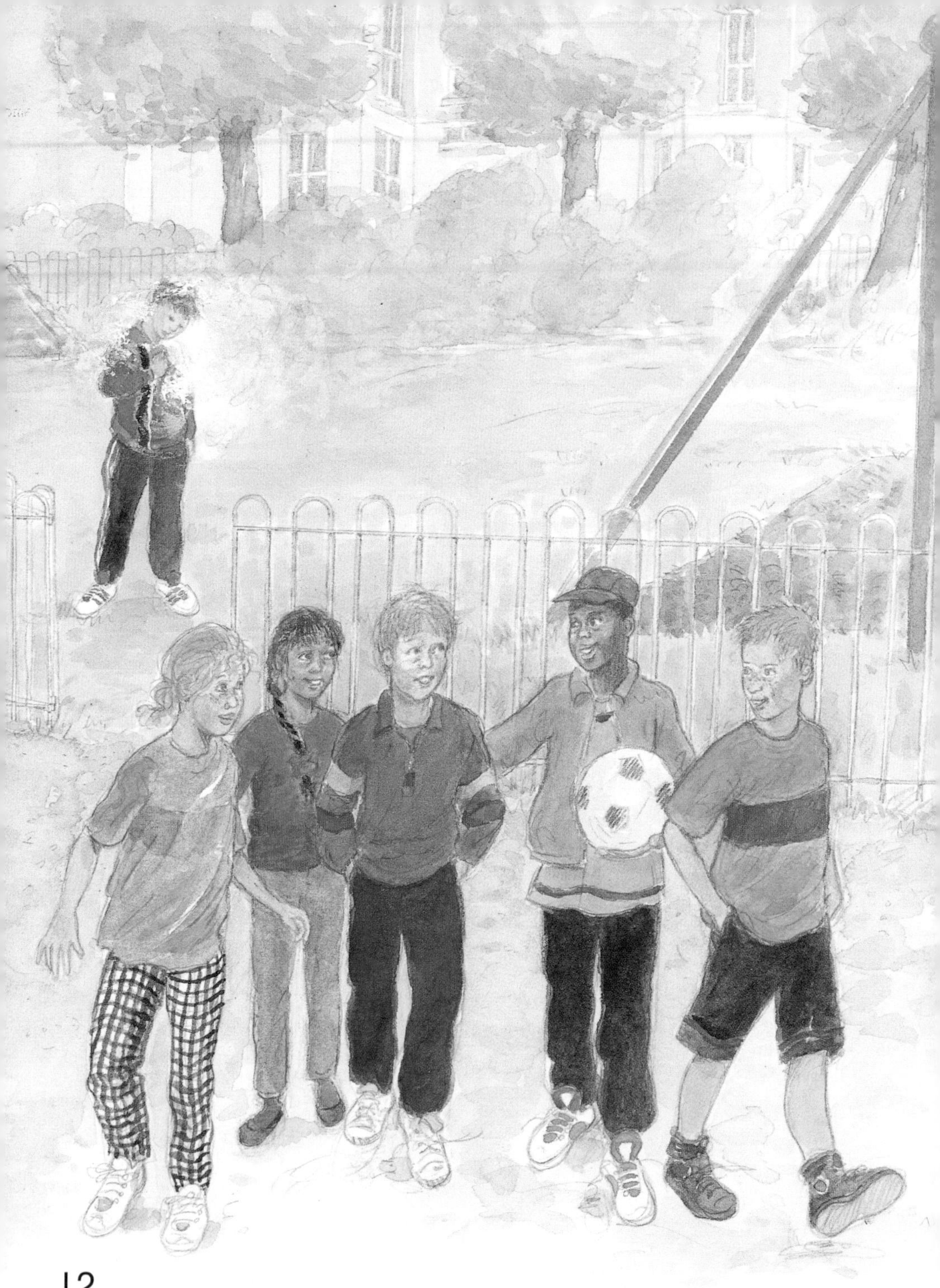